WHAT THE FEBRUARY?!

by @stevexoh

Published by Can Scorpions Smoke?
ISBN 978-1-3999-5098-5
© Stevexoh 2023

So, here's a splendid page of that rather dry and somewhat scary legal stuff that you get told you have to put in a book. So if you're going to read it then maybe turn it into a challenge and read it out loud in a silly voice or sing it like an opera or turn it into a rap.

Here goes...

Every effort has been made to reference and acknowledge appropriately those who have contributed to or influenced this collection.

All the challenges included are for life and not just for February.

What the February?!

In 2020 I decided to see what would happen if I set weird and wonderful challenges for my Instagram followers every day in the month of February. (I only chose February because it had the least amount of days so would be less work than any other month!)

Over the next four years people from around the world took part in over 100 challenges designed to stretch their creative muscles and make the world a little bit more wonky and mysterious.

It is important to me that my projects end intentionally, end well and end at a peak. So I decided that WTFEB 2023 would be the last one ever.

It was only during the last few days of the final WTFEB that I had the idea to compile all of the challenges into a book. And here it is.

In this book you will find 108 challenges from WTFEB 2020-2023. Please use this book in whatever way you choose. You can work through all of the challenges in order, or just pick a random page each day, or just do the ones you like, or leave it laying on a coffee table/in the toilet for unsuspecting guests to pick up, or completely forget you bought the book and leave it on a shelf gathering dust.

The only rule is that it is impossible to get it wrong.

Thanks as always for supporting my work.

@stevexoh

ICE CREAM VAN ART

Your challenge is to create some ice cream van art.

You know the kind of thing. Popular cartoon characters that are recognisable but also slightly off. Familiar but also not-quite-right in ways you can't quite put your finger on.

I once saw an amazing one of Rambo on an ice cream van in Cyprus so you certainly aren't limited to cartoon characters.

STRETCH CHALLENGE
Why not actually paint a real van with your not-quite-right ice cream van art?

WONKY LIFE PORTRAITS

Your challenge is to draw some wonky life
portraits: strange proportions, body positions
that wouldn't be possible for a real-life human
being and bits of anatomy that make no sense.

My own technique for doing wonky life portraits
is to start in the "wrong" place. Maybe begin
with a hand. Then a foot randomly on the page
An arm somewhere else. Then a head somewhere
towards the top. Only then does the magic
begin when you start to try and join up the
body parts.

STRETCH CHALLENGE
Find a real-life human being and ask if you
can draw them. Even better if you've never met
them before.

INVENT A PERFUME

Invent a totally unique and very strange perfume or aftershave. The name, the slogan, the bottle and, most importantly, the advert.

Take inspiration from the plethora of perfume adverts you will have no doubt seen during the festive season or memories of walking through those duty-free shops at airports or department store perfumeries.

STRETCH CHALLENGE
Make a high budget and totally confusing TV or radio advert for your perfume.

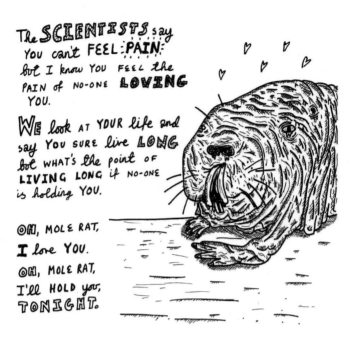

The SCIENTISTS say
YOU can't FEEL PAIN
but I know YOU FEEL the
PAIN of NO-ONE **LOVING**
YOU.

WE look AT YOUR life and
say YOU SURE live LONG
but WHAT'S the point OF
LIVING LONG if NO-ONE
is holding YOU.

OH, MOLE RAT,
I love YOU.
OH, MOLE RAT,
I'll HOLD you,
TONIGHT.

LOVE SONG FOR AN UNLOVED ANIMAL

You have been commissioned to write a love song for an unpopular animal. The type of creature that, for some reason, human beings have decided is ugly or stupid or pointless or annoying.

You could write a ballad for a bluebottle, a tune for a tick, a poem for a proboscis monkey. The main thing is that your song helps the animal feel some love.

You can create your lyrics in whatever form you like: type them, write them or illustrate them with flattering pictures of your chosen critter.

STRETCH CHALLENGE
Record your song or set it to music. Maybe try to find your animal and serenade it in person.

DAVE

MARGARET

SHOOTY JEFF

MRS KENSINGTON

NAME THE BIRDS

This challenge is set by guest challenger, musician and songwriter ERIC13.

It has come to Eric's attention that the birds of the world are a little disappointed not to have their own names. What if we humans were only known as *"person with black hair"* or *"orange person"*? Birds want names!

To rectify this, Eric's challenge is to name the birds. If you see a bird, give it a name. Pigeon fly by your window? Perhaps that is Michelle. Sparrow in the park? That could be Gerald. Crow at Kings Cross Station? Maybe that is Louise?

STRETCH CHALLENGE
Why not create an entire bird spotting book with pictures and facts about each one?

INSTRUCTIONS FOR LIVING A LIFE

Create a minimalist three-line poem to express your own instructions for living a life, inspired by the wonderful Mary Oliver poem "*Instructions for Living a Life*" shown above.

It could be profound, moving, mundane, odd, surreal. It doesn't matter as long as it is three lines long and instructs others how to live a life.

STRETCH CHALLENGE
Turn your poem into posters, post cards, t-shirts and share them with the world.

Give them away, sell them, go and post them through every door on your street.

word word word word word word word
word word word word word word word
word word word word word word word
word word word word word word word
word word word word word word word
word word word word word word word
word word word word word word word
word word word word word word word
word word word word word word word
word word word word word word word
word word word word word word word
word word word word word word word
word word word word word word word
word word word word word ......

DRAIN A WORD OF ITS MEANING

Pick a word and drain it of its meaning by saying it over and over and over and over again.

After some time, it will all go a bit weird and the word will start to detach itself from the thing it was previously associated with. You can drain it further by writing it down over and over again. Then saying it more. And so on. The more you can do it, the weirder it will get. Eventually it will just become a meaningless sound.

STRETCH CHALLENGE
Get a whole group of people together and see if it magnifies the draining effect. Why not arrange a mysterious meeting and spend an hour doing it en-masse?

REJECTED McDONALD'S MASCOT IDEAS

PERVY McPICKLE

LIEUTENANT LETTUCE

SIR LOIN THE
BURGER DISPENSING
BOVINE

HOT-BUN BRODY

FORGETFUL
FRY

SATANIC SHAKE

BAD MASCOTS

Your challenge is to design some terrible mascots for well-known brands, sports teams organisations. It is up to you how to interpret the word terrible.

They could be badly constructed, awfully designed or only vaguely resemble the thing they're supposed to be. Or they could be an inappropriate total mismatch for the brand. Or anything else you can think of.

You can create one mascot or a whole series. It is totally up to you.

STRETCH CHALLENGE
Create a real mascot outfit. And maybe go and get a photo of you wearing it outside the brand you have designed it for.

BENIGN INSULTS

The purpose of this challenge is to teach you the fine art of benign insults.

Insults that are so weird that you can use them without causing any offence. Simply come up with some strange and interesting insults that don't offend.

Take your time as this is a fine art to develop. Without practise one can accidentally infer something through one's choice of words.

Have fun you utter pencil sharpeners!

STRETCH CHALLENGE
Why not practice "live" with somebody, taking it in turns to throw benign insults at each other?

LAYERED SECRETS

This challenge involves creating a layered painting that contains your deepest secrets.

Start by painting/writing/drawing as many of your secrets as you can. Write things people don't know about you, things you think about, confessions, declarations of love for a secret crush, etc.

Take your time to lay out the secrets using different sizes, shapes, doodles, images.

Then cover them up, paint over them, make marks on top of them, obscure them with new bits of artwork. Use the size and shape of the secrets to influence the size, shape and colour of the cover-up.

Allow the bits that nobody will see to influence the bits that everyone will see.

Add detail to whatever you notice emerging and keep adding layers influenced by the previous layers.

When you get a sense that you are finished, share your creation with the world knowing you have bravely shared your secrets but nobody other than you knows what they are.

You could post your painting on social media, put it in your window, hang it on a tree or in a gallery.

This challenge works best with soft materials such as paints/pastels but you can use anything you like to do it - pens, pencils, paper cutting, etc.

STRETCH CHALLENGE
Experiment with scraping away the covering layers so that more of what lies beneath is revealed.

What is too much? What is not enough?

What is the exciting edge of disclosure/non-disclosure?

MAKE YOUR OWN CURRENCY

This challenge is set by guest challenger, writer and artist Nick Parker and is to make your own currency.

You can make a single note or an entire range of currency: coins, notes, crypto-currency, exchange rate, etc. It can be as simple or as complex as you like.

STRETCH CHALLENGE
See if you can buy something with your new currency. This could be as straightforward as exchanging it with someone else who is doing this challenge or as complicated as trying to use it in a shop.

BAD POETRY

It's time to create some bad poetry. Poems that you not only hate, but cringe as you write them. The kind of poem you want to hide away so that nobody will ever have to experience how terrible it is.

Aim for shallow and inconsequential subject matter, cheesy/mixed metaphors that don't make sense, inconsistent rhythm and line length and very desperate rhymes. And don't forget to come up with a title that is trying way too hard to be profound.

STRETCH CHALLENGE
Perform your poetry on the street or at an open mic.

TIME TRAVELLER

This challenge involves playing the role of a baffled time traveller.

On the hour, every hour, pretend you have just arrived from another time. Look totally confused. Ask people "What year is it? Who is the President?" etc. Pick up newspapers, look at the date and say "It cannot be!" Be fascinated and confused by everyday objects as if they are huge advances from the technology you are used to.

Or, if you have arrived from the future, do the opposite and scoff at modern tech as if it were from the dark ages. Do this for about a minute and then return to normal. Until the next hour.

STRETCH CHALLENGE
Can you do this for an entire day?

BARRY'S MYSTERY
MEAT IN A DRY BUN

- WE DON'T KNOW WHAT PART OF THE ANIMAL WE USE
- OR WHICH ANIMAL IT COMES FROM
- BUT IT'S CHEAP
- AND YOU'RE DRUNK

HONEST ADVERTS

Adverts often use a lot of spin to turn a not so-good product into an amazing product. Your challenge is to do the opposite.

Create an advert that is totally honest. An advert that does the advertising equivalent of over-sharing!

STRETCH CHALLENGE
Establish a full-on ad agency to provide these services to companies that want to embody a more honest approach to advertising.

GOOGLY-EYED GRAFFITI

This challenge was set by guest challenger, Lesley Graney of Random Acts of Nonsense and involves unleashing the awesome power of googly eyes onto the world.

Fruit, veg, inanimate objects, animate objects, people! Anything that is calling out for a bit of wobbly anthropomorphism.

If you don't have any googly eyes then simply draw some on paper and cut them out.

STRETCH CHALLENGE
Curate an exhibition of your googly-eyed creations.

NON-DOMINANT HAND MASTERPIECES

Try to recreate a classic piece of art using your non-dominant hand.

Try to make it as close to the original as possible so that the difference is barely detectable.

And if you are ambidextrous then maybe use a foot or your mouth or another body part for this challenge.

STRETCH CHALLENGE
See if you can pass off your masterpiece as an original to an art collector.

ANIMAL ALBUM COVERS

Re-create a classic album cover using only animals. It could be a Narwhal Nirvana baby, an Eel Elvis or an entire menagerie ensemble version of Sergeant Pepper.

As long as the humans are replaced by animals, anything goes.

STRETCH CHALLENGE
Write a brand new animal-related track listing for your album.

UNPLEASANT JOHN PRESENTS
SPONGFEST
☆ 2 0 1 8 ☆
THE NIAL OG 3 featuring Spurt Spakamak
UGLY JIMMY BUMHOLE
HISPANIC ROOM THE GLANDULAR BEACONS

THE MOSCHOPS STAGE
SPUNKY CAT
THE FOUR PLOPS
NIGEL WANK
GODDO FORCE 9

THE WAITROSE ESSENTIALS STAGE
CAPTAIN LIGHTBULB AND THE LUMBAGO CREW
V.A.T JESSICA JOCKSTRAP
DADDY LEPROSY LEO SAYER

THE ACTUAL GEOFF CAPES OUTSIDER TENT
THE SHREW FAMILY ROBINSON HORACE KNOWELS
HIPHOP REPLACEMENT SURGERY THE ODD DOGS
BETTY SCUMBAG AND THE HAUNTED PORK MANNEQUINS
ELECTRIC AUNT JEMIMA JETPACK GERIATRIC
MEOWATHON 2000 FRUMPY BUTTER MASSIVE DUMP

THE FAKE FESTIVAL

Create a poster for a festival that doesn't exist. The festival name, the band names, the stage names, the headliners, the unknown acts confined to playing at 1pm on the Thursday before everyone arrives.

You might include obscure/bizarre sponsors. You could include a spoken-word stage with strangely named poets and authors. Whatever you do, you don't actually have to make it happen so go for it big time.

STRETCH CHALLENGE
Why not go a step further and record a song by one of your fake acts? Or make a video animation of one of your acts performing at the festival to convince people even more that it is real.

BORING CARTOONS

The magic of a three-panel cartoon is that so much happens in such a small space. Stories unfurl, characters are altered, contexts shift. Magic, intrigue and mystery can emerge from three simple illustrated boxes.

Your challenge is to create the opposite. To create the most boring three-panel cartoon ever. Something that is utterly un-interesting. Something that makes the viewer give up after the second panel and not even bother moving on to the third. Something that makes the reader annoyed at the time they have wasted reading it.

And don't forget to give your boring cartoon a boring title.

STRETCH CHALLENGE
See how many boring three-panel cartoons you can create before you accidentally produce a good one.

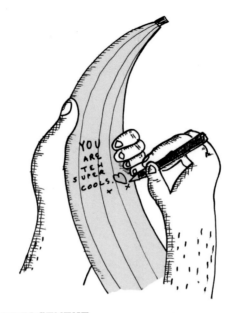

POSITIVE DEFACEMENT

This challenge is set by guest challenger, comedian, author and improviser Pippa Evans.

Try to write as many messages, to as many people as possible in your home, office, train, school, prison cell, etc without them noticing. Write them in their notebooks, on their napkins, even on their phones if you can. Anywhere you spot an opportunity.

The messages can be anonymous but they should be uplifting and encouraging. Your mission is to give someone a heart cockle-warming surprise in note form.

STRETCH CHALLENGE
Can you recruit an army of positive defacers to join you and create wide-spread joy?

MISCELLANEOUS ITEMS MOVIE SCENE

Recreate a famous movie scene with items you have lying around the home.

Think of an iconic scene from the world of cinema, have a look around for random objects and let the magic happen.

This famous scene from Jaws was re-created using a stapler, nail varnish remover bottle, tape, a pebble, card, beads, a USB card case and a j-cloth ocean.

STRETCH CHALLENGE
You might want to act out the scene or create a stop-motion animation with your items to fully immerse the viewer in re-living the original experience.

SKETCHNOTES FROM THE IMPORTANT CONFERENCE

Imagine you are at a big conference and have been paid to capture all of the inspirational leadership magic in illustrative form.

Include important buzzwords like MINDSET, VISION, STRATEGY alongside drawings of people working in synergetic collaborations. Don't forget to feature motivational phrases such as MOONSHOT and SUCCESSFULISATION as well as drawings of things such as people climbing mountains, lifting trophies or smiling at spread-sheets.

But, seeing as all conference sketch notes look the same, the main focus of your challenge is to make it look as weird as possible.

STRETCH CHALLENGE
Find a real conference and do it there.

FREELANCE DREAM DESIGNER

Become a freelance dream designer and design dreams for other people to have.

The most sought-after dream designers are those who design dreams that make total sense when the dreamer is asleep but make absolutely no sense at all on awaking. My own speciality is in designing weird anxiety dreams in which the dreamer obsesses about a really important task they have to complete only to realise, after a restless night, that it was all total nonsense.

You can illustrate your dream or simply write a script.

STRETCH CHALLENGE
Share your design with others and see if they can have your dream tonight. Do remember to invoice them for this service.

BAD FAN ART

Your challenge is to produce some truly bad fan art. It can be of a celebrity, a band, a literary legend, a sports person, a cartoon character, anyone. The most important thing is that it embodies all the hallmarks of bad fan art: weird proportions and only vaguely recognisable because the bizarre caption gives a clue as to who it is.

Good bad fan art also portrays the object of fandom in weird, surreal or overly-elevated positions of omnipotence or strength. (e.g. as some sort of guru, peace-maker, a uniter of people, a magnet to cute animals, super powers, etc.)

STRETCH CHALLENGE
Send your bad fan art to the celebrity.

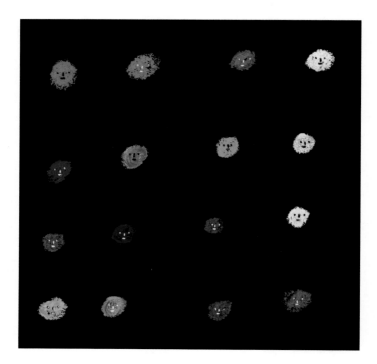

THE LITTLE CREATURES THAT SIT IN YOUR HEART

This challenge is set by guest challenger, artist jdwoof. Jo invites you to draw the little creatures that sit in your heart.

You can use any medium you like so don't feel limited to drawing. You could use paint, clay, pastels, other materials, movement, dance, etc.

STRETCH CHALLENGE
Try drawing the creatures you imagine that sit in somebody else's heart. A friend, a family member, enemy, somebody similar or different, an animal.

And if you want to take it further, let your creatures and their creatures interact to see what happens.

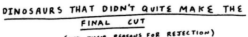

DINOSAURS THAT DIDN'T QUITE MAKE THE
FINAL CUT
(AND THEIR REASONS FOR REJECTION)

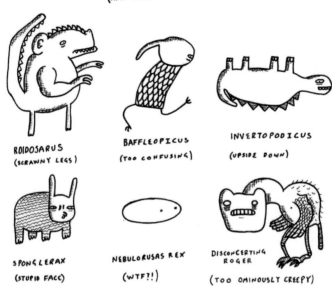

ROIDOSARUS
(SCRAWNY LEGS)

BAFFLEOPICUS
(TOO CONFUSING)

INVERTOPODICUS
(UPSIDE DOWN)

SPONGLERAX
(STUPID FACE)

NEBULORUSAS REX
(WTF?!)

DISCONCERTING
ROGER
(TOO OMINOUSLY CREEPY)

REJECTED DINOSAUR IDEAS

Most people know of Triceratops, Stegosaurus, T-Rex and so on. But not many people know that, at the dawn of time, there was an X-Factor type talent contest to filter the plethora of species who applied to be dinosaurs down to a handful that would become the popular ones.

Your job is to honour those who didn't make the final cut and educate us as to the reasons why. Simply draw or paint your beasts and include their reasons for rejection.

STRETCH CHALLENGE
Why not create a rejected dinosaur poster with loads of them on it? Or build a model of one. Or an animation.

EVERYDAY CARTOONS

This challenge is inspired by an Ivan Brunetti cartooning exercise and is to create a single panel cartoon from your everyday experiences.

STEP 1. Throughout the day make a note of at least eight random phrases you overhear (on TV, on the radio, in a cafe, etc).

STEP 2. On 8 different pieces of paper, without thinking too much about it, draw the following (just images, no words):

i.   The funniest thing.
ii.   The saddest thing.
iii. Something sexy.
iv.   Something abstract.
v.   Something scary.

vi.   Something boring or mundane.
vii. Something you saw earlier today.
viii. Something you saw in a dream.

STEP 3. When you have all 8 drawings and phrases, lay them all out in front of you and mix and match the words with the images.

Pay attention to when something 'clicks' and the combination elicits laughter, confusion, irony, profundity, etc.

STEP 4. (optional) Share your finished combination with the world on social media post in your window/submit to the New Yorker.

STRETCH CHALLENGE
Combine more than one of your finished cartoons to create a three-panel comic strip.

IMPROVISED GIRAFFES

This challenge is to create a giraffe from whatever items you have lying around the home office/etc.

Try to capture as much detail as possible in your giraffes; the proportions, the markings, the aesthetics.

Ideally your improvised giraffes should be able to trick a zoologist into thinking it is real.

STRETCH CHALLENGE
Create a tower (the collective word for this species) of giraffes of various shapes or sizes.

EDUCATIONAL FREEART ZINE

Create a homemade educational zine to leave in public for others to find and digest.

Your subject matter should aim to be as weird obscure/specialised as possible.

You could write a brief history of metal hoops, a detailed guide to educating crabs, step-by step instructions for appearing more important than you actually are. It's totally up to you.

When you have made your zine, the final task is to leave it somewhere for people to find. A coffee shop. On the bus. In a library. Then walk away from it knowing that today you have made a difference to the lives of human beings.

STRETCH CHALLENGE
Photocopy your zine and leave loads of them around.

BAD THINGS THAT DON'T EXIST

This challenge is set by guest challenger, the artist Kazland.

Kaz's challenge is simply to create something in response to the prompt *"Bad things that don't exist"*. It is totally up to you what you do.

STRETCH CHALLENGE
Why not create a series of responses to the prompt? Or write a book. Or make a short film about a number of bad things that don't exist.

CLASSIFIEDS: FREE STUFF

WANTED

Electronic David Hasslehoff simulator. Any model pre 1994 with charger.

Amusing eggs. Any species. Must be amusing. No time wasters.

Right hand strawberry-blonde sideburn needed urgently. Between 0.1-0.5kg/m3 density. Will pay for fast shipping.

Photos of Hilda Ogden. Any era considered.

Oscilating Leg Harp. Ideally models with in-built ego-modulator and side-hustle.

Jokes about bears. Short ones, long ones. I don't mind.

Portable silence. Must be absolute and easy to transport.

Front wheel of mouse trike. Ideally with at least 2mm of tread left on tyres.

Compliments. Any welcome. Positive comments on appearance, intellect, odour or other aspects of self.

OFFERED

Noel Gallagher signed photo. Signed by Noel Edmonds. Free to loving home.

Left handed crab pacifier. Works on all European species. NOT FOR USE ON LOBSTERS.

Terrifying dolls heads. Not for the faint-hearted. My nerves cannot take their creepy stares any more.

Various small objects. A wide variety of shapes and colours.

Unused bath water. I ran it but didn't have time for a bath. Approx 110ltr with radox bubbles.

Song for a dog called Benji. I wrote it for him and he didn't like it. Free to a more appreciative dog.

Three piece prune suit. A very smart outfit, cotton weave with fresh prunes stapled to prominent areas. Size: medium

Fake smiles. Useful in many social situations.

SURREAL SWAP SHOP

What strange stuff do you have lying around your home/office/studio that you could offer up? And what strange stuff would you like to swap it for?

You might no longer want your signed William Shatner disco record but need the right leg of a mannequin. If so, this is the challenge for you.

Let the world know what you want, what you need and see what happens. Share your offers and/or requests on social media, free-ad websites or the local newspaper.

STRETCH CHALLENGE
Become a surreal swap shop match-maker and try to match offers and requests.

□ CRAP □ NOT CRAP □ CRAP □ NOT CRAP
□ CRAP □ NOT CRAP □ CRAP □ NOT CRAP
□ CRAP □ NOT CRAP □ CRAP □ NOT CRAP
□ CRAP □ NOT CRAP □ CRAP □ NOT CRAP

CRAP FACES

This challenge is to draw some crap faces. Draw an 8-box grid on a piece of paper. In each box try really hard to draw a crap face. A really terrible picture. The worst one you can possibly do. One that you'd rather the world would never see.

When you have drawn all 8 faces, review your work and rate each face as CRAP or NOT CRAP. But be honest — if there is a face that you like, even just ever so slightly, you must mark it NOT CRAP.

STRETCH CHALLENGE
Can you do 100 crap faces without accidentally doing one you or another human being consider not crap?

RE-BUSINIFY YOUR GOAL PURPOSE

#1

GER FUNKADELLIC Jr
Best selling author of Un-timidifying your autheticator factor

Re-Businify Your Goal Purpose

by **Ger Funkadellic Jr** (Author)

⭐⭐⭐⭐½ ˅ 2,174

Hardcover	Paperback
£7.16	£9.01 ✓prime
13 Used from £7.16	29 Used from £3.25
2 New from £48.95	19 New from £6.99

Top reviews from United Kingdom

👤 Norman Badreview

⭐☆☆☆☆ **Made me vomit for 3 days**
Reviewed in the United Kingdom 14th September 2021
Verified Purchase

I am bamboozled, baffled, flummoxed and embroiled in somewhat of an existential crisis at all of the 5 star reviews that this utter waste of trees has received. I can only assume that these reviews have been written by members of Mr Funkadellic Jrs cult of "Humanagement"!!!

I vomited instantly on reading the titles of the chapters on the index page: "Go cry on sombody else's spreadsheet", "Envision the soup ladel of your success" and "Imaginate your truley orgasmic leadership purposition." Once I recovered enough to read on (the glossy cover actually wipes clean remarkably well, which is why I have given one star!) I was horrified to be subjected to a firehose of humblebrags in which the author claims to have invented the question mark in order to promote "empowered individualised expansion", tells the story of how he advised the Dali Llama on Lean Six Sigma to "guru up a level" and tale after tale of stopping in the street to help the homeless with his patented "Bum's Rush"™ actualisation methodology (accompanied with pictures of a grinning Mr Funkadelic with his arm around a poor confused looking vagrant who would clearly have preferred £1 towards a hot meal. I not only advise you not to buy this travesty of human evolution but I also urge the UN to take swift and effective action to destroy every copy.

IMAGINARY BOOK REVIEW

Write a book review for a book that doesn't exist. It can be a novel, a technical manual, a self-help book. It can be a book you love, a book you hate. As long as the book doesn't actually exist it can be whatever genre you like.

Just make sure that it gives valuable information to others who might be considering buying the book.

STRETCH CHALLENGE
Why not also draw or mock up a cover for your book? Chapter titles, endorsements, etc. Add your book and review to Goodreads or other review sites to baffle more people.

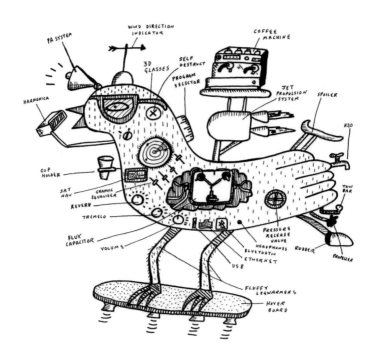

PIMP A CRITTER

Can you take an everyday creature and pimp it? "Improve" it with technology. Bling it up! Make it multi-media! Upgrade it to be compatible with modern life with interfaces, gauges, dials and gadgets.

If it's an unpopular animal then try to re brand it so it appeals to a bigger audience.

STRETCH CHALLENGE
Create an entire instruction manual for your critter or an animation or a comic strip to demonstrate its multiple functions.

GO TO WORK AS A DEAD ROCK STAR

This challenge is set by guest challenger, speaker and eco-innovator Mark Shayler. Mark invites you to go to work (or school/college/ etc) dressed as a dead rock star.

As well as your appearance try to embody everything about this person - attitude, voice, catch-phrases, performance. And if you don't have a workplace to go to then simply go out in public or hang around at home for the day dressed as your person.

STRETCH CHALLENGE
Get others to join in. Maybe all dress as the same person. Or as different members of a band.

DESTROY YOUR ART

Create some beautiful art and then destroy it!

It could be a sketch you shred, a drawing you disintegrate, a painting you pulverise, a sculpture you smash. Be as creative with the destruction as you are with the creation.

It sounds simple (and it might be!) but at the heart of this challenge is the tension created between making and breaking. How does knowing that you will destroy your creation affect the process of making it? Can you take great care to make something beautiful knowing that it will no longer exist soon after it is completed?

STRETCH CHALLENGE
You could destroy an entire body of work.

ANIMAL REDUNDANCIES

Nature is having a tough time and, to help cut costs, is having to sadly make some species redundant. But, as nature is a good employer, they are helping the laid-off animals find some new suitable employment and have recruited you to help.

However, you are not very good at your job and end up assigning them to terribly inappropriate roles (e.g. a Tiger checkout assistant: growls at customers, paws too big to swipe stuff, wants to eat the food, can't stand upright for long). So pick an animal and do your worst to re-assign it to a new job.

STRETCH CHALLENGE
Re-assign as many animals as possible and become a top animal redundancy recruiter.

Switch

it

all

OFF

ANALOGUE DAY

This challenge requires you to switch off and not use any digital devices from the moment you finish reading this page.

You can still use analogue stuff: typewriters, letters, ordinary doorbells, even old-school landline phones. As long as it isn't digital.

You are allowed to switch on your digital devices at 11:59pm this evening in your own timezone.

STRETCH CHALLENGE
Try this for longer than a day. Or maybe fine yourself each time you use something digital and give the money raised to a charity or somebody in need.

EVERYDAY LYRICS

Your challenge is to pick lyrics from a song and see how many times you can insert them into your day without anyone knowing what you're doing.

Drop them into a phone call, an e-mail, a social media post, a greeting to the postal worker/ delivery driver, or on a cold call. Sneak them into some client work or a college assignment, a keynote talk, a bedtime story with the kids or simply insert them into a piece of art. It doesn't matter where or when or how, just as often as you can throughout the day.

STRETCH CHALLENGE
You can add a scoring system, giving yourself points/rewards dependent on how many times you manage to use your lyric.

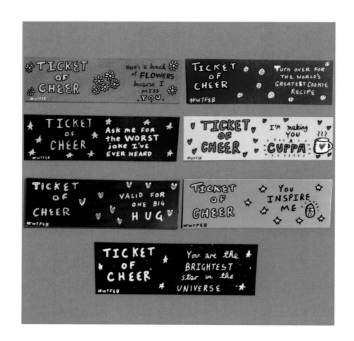

TICKETS OF CHEER

This challenge is set by guest challengers Reasons to Be Cheerful and is to make three tickets of cheer to give to others. It can say whatever you want and look however you want it to, as long as it aims to bring cheer to the person or people (or animals) who receive it.

You can hand your tickets to somebody else, put them through the door, tag somebody on social media, photograph and e-mail them, put them in the post or leave them out in public for people to find.

STRETCH CHALLENGE
Why not create a "cascade of cheer" that encourages recipients to pass on their own tickets of cheer to another person?

LOW BUDGET DISNEY

This challenge is to create a low budget Disney-esque* movie.

Whereas the average Disney production costs around $190M you have $0. The characters must be made using things you find around you. The scenery must be created by you. The music and sound effects must be made by you. And, as you have no budget at all for editing, it ideally must all be done in one take.

Don't forget the compelling characters, the fantastical scenery and the traditional hero's journey story structure. And remember to throw in some sort of moral lesson for the kids.

STRETCH CHALLENGE
Why not pitch your idea to Disney/Pixar/etc?

* With Disney lawyers in mind I must emphasise that this is a Disney-ESQUE production!

STRIPPED BACK SKETCHES

This challenge is a twist on a classic Ivan Brunetti cartooning exercise. Pick something you think that you can't draw or don't enjoy drawing. Set a timer for 4 minutes. You must use the WHOLE of those 4 minutes to draw your thing. Then set a timer for 2 minutes and do the same. Then repeat the same process for 1 minute. Then 30 seconds. Then 15 seconds. And finally 7.5 seconds.

Take a look back at your drawings. Which one do you like the most? Which one was most fun to draw and why? How did your image change as the time limit shortened?

STRETCH CHALLENGE
Do it more than once with a number of different things. Maybe a self portrait?

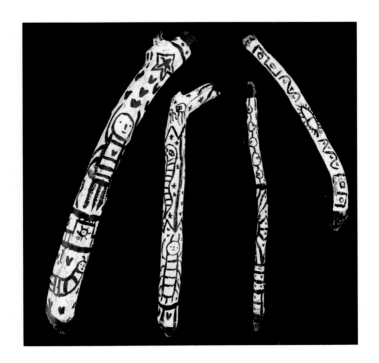

PAINTED STICKS

This challenge is all about painting sticks. It could be a stick you find outside on the street or in the park or in a garden. Or it could be a stick that is in your home — a broomstick, a walking stick, a lollipop stick, etc.

Rather than trying to decide what to paint on your stick, let your stick guide you. Simply let its contours, lumps and bumps suggest shapes, lines and images. And of course, if you don't have paints you can use pens, crayons, pencils, anything.

STRETCH CHALLENGE
Why not create a number of different sticks and set up a market stall to give them to people?

DRINK A GLASS OF WATER IN PUBLIC

This challenge might be a profound experience that exposes the bizarre nature of the human condition, cracking open a profound vein of insight and creative expression...or it may be utterly pointless.

The challenge is simply to drink a glass of water in public. Maybe start by standing out side your home/work. Then maybe onto a busy high-street or into a shopping centre or wander around a park. Just hold the glass and take sips as you naturally would at home.

How does it feel? What do you imagine other people think about you doing this?

STRETCH CHALLENGE
Invite a friend or a group of friends to create a big, wandering glass of water drinking collective.

LOVELY LETTERS

This challenge is set by guest challenger, performer, writer and activist Revolting Rosy Pendlebaby.

Rosy's challenge is simply to leave a nice letter somewhere for a stranger to find. Your letter could be some kind words, some wisdom, some delightful weirdness.

Decorate your letter with drawings, glitter, cut-outs, photos — whatever you feel like. As long as it will be something nice for somebody you don't know to find.

STRETCH CHALLENGE
Write a whole series of lovely letters for strangers and see if you can brighten an entire community's day.

A YES SAFARI

This challenge is to set yourself a period of time to go on a YES Safari. During your safari you will say "YES" to literally everything. People, signs, adverts, impulses, alleyways, invitations, gut-feelings, etc.

See what new adventures you have in the time frame you set. You can choose any duration for a YES safari although 1 hour+ is probably best to experience the exponential power of YES.

STRETCH CHALLENGE
Can you extend your YES safari over an entire day? Or a week? Or longer?

If you would like a counterpoint to this then try the NO safari challenge elsewhere in the book.

ILLUSTRATE A SONG

Your challenge is to illustrate a song.

It could be a line from a song, a verse from a song, an entire song. It is totally up to you.

It could be a song with simple, obvious lyrics. Or a more mysterious and abstract song that you improvise a drawing to.

As always, you can paint, draw, sculpt, dance or do whatever you want in response to your song.

STRETCH CHALLENGE
Illustrate an entire album.

THIS PLAQUE IS DEDICATE TO THE
HUNDREDS oF PEOPLE
WHO MYSTERIOUSLY DISAPPEARED
MOMENTS AFTER READING THIS
PLAQUE

PECULIAR PLAQUES

Create a weird, confusing, baffling plaque and install it somewhere.

It could be a strange dedication, an unusual historical fact, a nonsensical motivational phrase. As long as it makes people stop and say "uh?" it can be anything.

You can make your plaque out of paper, card, wood, metal, etc. Whatever you have to hand. Once you've got it then install it on a bench, a wall, a building and leave knowing that you have made the world that little bit wonkier today.

STRETCH CHALLENGE
If you have the budget, why not get your plaque professionally made?

DRAW YOUR MIND

This challenge is to simply draw your mind.

Pause for a moment, notice what is there and draw it in whatever form you like.

It could be words, images or something weirder and more abstract such as a sculpture or an interpretive dance. It's your mind so you can't get it wrong!

STRETCH CHALLENGE
Offer to draw the minds of others. Friends, family, co-workers, random people on the street. See how accurately you can represent their inner world.

BATTENBERG MAN

BATTENBERG SUPERHERO

This challenge is set by guest challenger Ben Murphie (aka The Prince of Battenberg). Ben's challenge is to draw, paint or print a picture of your favourite superhero and then colour them in using as much PINK and YELLOW as possible.

Label your Battenberg superhero with the adjectives that best describe how they make you feel and display the picture in a public space. It could be a workplace or favoured domestic setting, a park, a pub or anywhere where it can be viewed by others.

STRETCH CHALLENGE
Dress in an entirely pink and yellow outfit for one day and collect adjectives used to describe your appearance when out and about.

"A great leader is like a tea bag; they infuse their followers with their flavour and aren't afraid to drip a little when removed."

@stevexoh

#WTFEB

BECOME A THOUGHT LEADER FOR THE DAY

Today's challenge is to become a "Thought Leader" for the day. To motivate and educate people with your overly-simplistic and largely nonsensical wisdom. To spend the day helping those who are far less guru-like than yourself improve their lives by sharing the benefit of your life experience and knowledge in the field of self development/leadership/business/etc.

You could write some clever sounding nonsense posts on social media to lure people into your omnipotent light, or comment on other's posts in order to slip in your own models/theories. Or you could record a motivational speech to make people laugh/cry/gasp/pass-out when they hear how you have hacked life and how they can do it too.

STRETCH CHALLENGE
Host a webinar/live broadcast so people can drink the wisdom direct from the tap.

EXPERIMENTS IN THE PHILOSOPHY OF EVERYDAY LIFE

This challenge comprises 4 mini-challenges taken from the weird little book *"Astonish Yourself"* by Roger-Pol Droit. Pick one or try them all.

DRINK WHILST URINATING. Drink a glass of water without pausing whilst you urinate until you experience a weird synchronicity between input and output.

PEEL AN APPLE IN YOUR MIND. In as much detail as possible from selecting the fruit through to choosing your tools to completing the task.

COUNT TO 1,000 OUT LOUD. Simply count to 1,000 out loud.

RANT FOR TEN MINUTES IN FRONT OF THE MIRROR. Rant about something you think is worth ranting about for 10 minutes without stopping.

STRETCH CHALLENGE
Do all four challenges daily for a week.

FANTASY HEIST CREW

Form a fantasy heist crew like in those heist movies. What roles does your heist crew need? The muscle? The brains? The whistler? The weirdo? The one who knows how to fill a pepper pot without spilling it?

The advantage you have is that you are not limited to reality. You can recruit from the world of celebrities, films, cartoons, books, politics, living, dead, animals, inanimate objects, etc. And don't forget to recruit for weirdly specific roles.

STRETCH CHALLENGE
Pick an appropriate fantasy heist target for your crew. In fact, write an entire story that can easily be turned into yet another heist film.

OUTRAGEOUS CLAIMS

This challenge is to make outrageous claims throughout the day. Things like *"I invented the bullet point!"*, *"I'm the one who turned dogs and cats against each other!"*, *"I'm the one who told Freddie Mercury that he'd look good with a moustache!"* The more outrageous the claim, the better. And don't back down if you meet doubters, just double-down on your boast.

STRETCH CHALLENGE
Post your outrageous claims on social media. Or write a blog about them. Or do a TED talk telling your story. Just remember, don't tell anyone that you are doing this challenge.

UNDER THE TABLE

This challenge is set by guest challenger, author, journalist and speaker JP Flintoff.

JP's challenge is to take an interesting selfie under a table. It could be at home, at work, somewhere else. You might even take a table on a day trip to an interesting or unusual location for a special WTFEB under-the-table photoshoot.

STRETCH CHALLENGE
Why not create a diary of your day under various tables?

YOUR BEAUTIFUL SANDCASTLE

WILL BE OBLITERATED BY THE SEA

DE-MOTIVATIONAL POSTERS

Motivational posters have become a big thing. You know, the ones often seen in corporate settings that have photos of mountains and say things like *"Strive for the summit"*.

Well, your job today is to do the opposite and create some de-motivational posters.

Paint, draw or use any medium you like for these. As long as they sap human enthusiasm they are perfect.

STRETCH CHALLENGE
Put up your de-motivational poster somewhere. Or get a load printed to sell. You might make a huge amount of money from this brand new niche industry.

DARK FORGERIES

Imagine you have been given the mission to replace an iconic bit of art with a forgery but you can only do this when the lights of the gallery are out. And, for some reason, you have to do it live and in situ. Well it's that kinda thing.

You can get all of your materials ready before the lights go out but once you begin you cannot look at the paper/canvas until it is completed Use whatever materials you want - pen, paint, pencil, clay, etc.

If you don't have a dark room you can maybe wear a blindfold or simply close your eyes.

STRETCH CHALLENGE
Try to hang your dark forgery in a gallery or sell it on the internet as the original and see if you can get away with it.

SING YOUR DAY

This challenge is to sing your day. Whatever you are doing — sing about it. The more mundane the better.

If you are making breakfast then turn it into a musical. If you are typing at your computer then turn it into an opera. If you are trying to get to sleep then turn it into a pumping rock ballad. The key is to try and sing as much of your day as you can, simply narrating it in musical form.

STRETCH CHALLENGE
Try to enrol others into this challenge. Delivery drivers need to sing for your signature, work meetings need to become close harmony acapella experiences, arguments need to become love duets.

DANCING IN PUBLIC

This challenge is simply to dance in public.

Dance in the street, on the train, in a meeting or job interview, in a restaurant. Feel free to interpret the words "dancing" and "public" in whatever way you want to.

STRETCH CHALLENGE
Why not put down a hat and collect donations for your dance? Or encourage others to join you to form an improvised dance troupe.

INVERTED PORTRAITURE

This challenge is set by guest challenger, Kath of Feel More Creative and is to undertake some inverted portraiture.

Inverted portraiture is the art of taking a photo of somebody when they are upside down and presenting it as if it were a perfectly normal photo. The objective is to create a moment of uncertainty for the viewer who can't quite tell what isn't right with the picture.

You can be the upside down model in your photo or you can take photos of others.

STRETCH CHALLENGE
Change all of your social media profile pictures to be your inverted portrait.

SINGLE BREATH CINEMA

Your challenge is to recreate a famous movie poster in one breath. Pick your movie poster, prepare your materials, get everything ready before you begin and then you have one full breath (in and out) to complete your artwork.

You can begin the moment your in-breath begins and you must stop the moment your out-breath stops. (Please prioritise breathing in again over finishing your artwork!)

Remember, it is impossible to get this wrong so you can do it with whatever level of breath holding capability you have.

STRETCH CHALLENGE
Create a series of film posters. Experiment with different breathing techniques for each.

START A NICHE MEMBERSHIP CLUB

This challenge is to start a bizarre niche membership club. It could be to appreciate your favourite animal, or protect a certain flavour of crisps or to raise awareness of a minor, largely inconsequential day-to-day niggle or worry you have (e.g. The Society for Kettle Fur awareness.) The more niche and bizarre the better.

Create a logo, a membership card, a manifesto and posters for your secret society. Make it so compelling that people can't help but want to join you.

STRETCH CHALLENGE
Make a promotional campaign and see how many people you can get to join your society.

BURIED TREASURE

Your challenge is to bury some treasure.

Find or make a treasure chest and put stuff in it. It could contain little items you have laying around or things you make. Lovely things, mysterious things, strange things.

Then go and bury it. If it isn't possible to actually bury it then just hide it somewhere out of sight, but leave some clues as to where it is to reward the curious. You might even draw a map to put up nearby.

STRETCH CHALLENGE
Add instructions for people to take an object and leave an object to create a perpetual never-ending treasure trove.

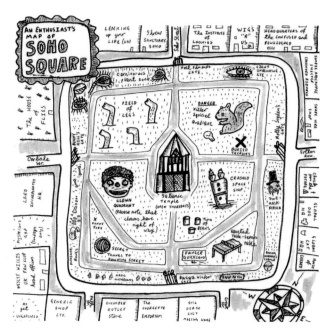

MAPS OF MYSTERY

The purpose of this challenge is to confuse inspire/amuse others through the process of bizarre map making.

Use a real-life area as the inspiration for your map but then add all sorts of weird and wonderful things to it. Strange caves, buried treasure, unusual shops, mythical beasts, hidden tunnels. Anything that spices up the reality of the place.

You might use a park as your inspiration, a high street, a building, an entire town.

The final step of this challenge is to leave your map near the location for somebody to find.

STRETCH CHALLENGE
Create a number of copies of your map to distribute.

PREPARE A MEAL OF JUST ONE COLOUR

This challenge is set by guest challenger, author and facilitator Robert Poynton. It is pretty self-explanatory: prepare a meal of just one colour.

It is an invitation to use the constraint of colour to come up with something you'd never normally eat/serve/imagine.

STRETCH CHALLENGE
Why not extend this challenge over an entire day? A blue breakfast, a lilac lunch, a danube dinner?

NO SAFARI

This challenge is to set yourself a period of time to go on a NO Safari. During your safari you will say "NO" to literally everything.

People, signs, adverts, impulses, alleyways, invitations, gut-feelings. Everything. See what new adventures you have in the time frame you set. You can choose any duration for a NO safari although 1 hour+ is probably best in order to experience the dampening power of NO.

STRETCH CHALLENGE
Can you extend your NO safari over an entire day? Or a week? Or longer?

If you would like a counterpoint to this then try the YES safari challenge elsewhere in the book.

IMPERFECT PORTRAITS

Draw an imperfect portrait of somebody without any thought as to whether it looks like them. Just draw it quickly, without thinking about it too much and treat any resemblance as a total coincidence.

If you don't think you can draw portaits then you are totally qualified for this challenge. If you think you can draw portraits then you may need to work a little harder to nurture the imperfection. Either way, consider any inaccuracies as simply an expression of your natural style.

STRETCH CHALLENGE
Offer your services to strangers on the street.

OPEN AN ART GALLERY

Open your own art gallery and challenge the societal conventions of what a gallery is. It could be in your window, in your kitchen, in your toilet. It could be outside on a bench or in a bush. (In 2019 I installed #HBGOA on a central London railway bridge and David Shrigley once exhibited in a skip.)

Your gallery might have just one bit of artwork or may be an extensive collection. All you need to do is to label it into existence and, hey presto, you are now a professional exhibiting artist/gallery owner.

STRETCH CHALLENGE
Gather art from other artists for a group exhibition or register a website or social media account for your gallery.

BODY PART BALLADS

Write a song for a body part.

It might be a part of you that you love.
Or a part of you that you have a difficult
relationship with. Or a part of you that often
goes unappreciated and you want to show some
love.

It could be a ditty about a diaphragm, a verse
about a vertebra, a tune about a toe, etc.

You can simply write some lyrics or sing the
song or have an entire orchestral arrangement.

STRETCH CHALLENGE
You could record a music video for your body
part or release your track to the world on
Spotify or other streaming platforms.

CAN YOU HELP?

This challenge is set by guest challenger, musician and people enthusiast Katie Elliott and requires you to ask for help. You could ask somebody in person, put up a sign or post your request on social media.

It could be anything - wanting to know how to do something, an introduction to someone, an outrageous solution to a problem, a bit of encouragement.

As long as it's something that you would find genuinely helpful and something you would NEVER usually ask for help with.

STRETCH CHALLENGE
Why not become a match-maker for other people's requests and offers of help.

IT IS HARDER TO GROW
Out at Sea
ALL ITEMS OF VALUE HAVE BEEN REMOVED
Chance encounters matter
Don't be a tourist
Be an explorer
@STEVExeh
#WTFB

FRANKENSTEIN'S POEMS

This challenge is to create a poem from bits and pieces of text you find lying around and phrases you encounter throughout your day.

You could take cuttings from newspapers or photos of billboards, signs, tattoos, finance reports, t-shirts - anything! Once you have a good collection of stuff then take them back to your lab and assemble your very own poetry monster.

STRETCH CHALLENGE
Perform your poem in a public space. A park, an office, a street corner, an open mic, etc.

MUNDANE SUPER HEROES

Design a mundane super hero whose superpowers, whilst somewhat helpful, are very specific and only really applicable to rare and largely inconsequential situations.

For example, I have the super power to be able to accurately estimate a 50g quantity of butter, without scales, within a tolerance of +/- 2g.

Come up with your own mundane super hero. Design their costumes, draw comic strips of them. Maybe design their enemies who want to thwart their efforts to marginally improve the lives of very few people in very specific situations.

STRETCH CHALLENGE
Become your mundane super hero for the day.

100 ANIMALS

Draw 100 of the same animal on the same page.

It is that simple. Nothing more to it than that. You may find it therapeutic. You may find it meditative. You may find it the most frustrating/boring/mundane thing ever. Whatever your experience is - that's what this challenge is for you. The only rules are that there must be 100, they must be of the same animal and they must be on the same page.

STRETCH CHALLENGE
Why not go for 200, 500, 1,000? Or draw 100 really detailed, complicated animals.

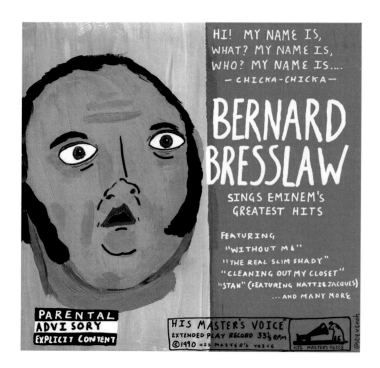

OBSCURE ALBUM COVERS

Create an obscure album cover.

Imagine you are flicking through a crate of second-hand records and suddenly come across something incredibly bizarre. The type of album that makes you say *"What the?! I never knew they did that!"* Roger Moore mangles the Sound of Music? Sinatra sings Slayer? Theresa May's spoken word Tupac tribute album?

Go wild with weird crossovers and genre mismatches that delve into the unknown recesses of a celebrity's body of work.

STRETCH CHALLENGE
Mock up an actual album cover and go and leave it in a second hand record shop or charity shop.

TROOTHIES™

This challenge is set by guest challenger, author Amy Kean. Amy's challenge is to make yourself a Troothie™ - a truth smoothie. A combination of weird and wonderful ingredients that, when you drink it, makes you share a vaguely controversial truth that people might not like.

Draw/paint/sculpt your Troothie™ then list and label the ingredients. (Amy's Troothie™ would contain whipped cream, peaches, miso paste and streaky bacon.)

Then share the vaguely controversial truth that you cannot help but share having drunk it. (Amy's example: *"I feel compelled to say the Beatles weren't even that good."*)

STRETCH CHALLENGE
Actually make your Troothie™ and drink it to see what happens. (Please do not drink toxic/harmful substances.)

A SILENT ADVANCE

This challenge is simply to bring your silence to the world. Instead of a silent retreat, when we go somewhere to be silent, you are to do the opposite and bring your silence into everyday places.

Shops, work, school, parks, bars, restaurants, etc.

Any place where a gentle, silent presence will have an effect on those who witness it.

STRETCH CHALLENGE
See if you can get others to join your silent advance without using any words to explain what it is.

Inside the sign:

PUBLIC NOTICE

DO NOT READ THIS SIGN

IF YOU ACCIDENTALLY READ THIS SIGN THEN PLEASE
CALL THE NUMBER ON THE OTHER SIGN
IMMEDIATELY

A GENTLE RE-WEIRDENING

This challenge is to gently re-weirden the world in order to create wonder.

To create something subtle but unexpected. To make something that causes a moment of *"eh?"* Something that triggers a moment of doubting one's assumptions about the nature of reality. Something out of place. A weird sign. A weird art installation. Some googly eyes stuck onto something. A weirdly dressed human statue.

It can be anything, as long as it creates a wonderfully wonky pattern interruption to the day of any human beings that encounter it.

STRETCH CHALLENGE
Why not create a re-weirdening trail with more than one exhibit to see if you can slowly freak people out as they walk.

WONKY SELF PORTRAITS

Your challenge is to create a very wonky and terribly inaccurate self-portrait.

Misshapen limbs, bizarre proportions, joints moving in ways that they couldn't possibly move in real life. But don't just chuck something on a page, this challenge is to take great care in producing something that is downright weird but also bears a vaguely passing resemblance to you.

STRETCH CHALLENGE
Why not create a series of self-portraits to show your typical day-in-your-life?

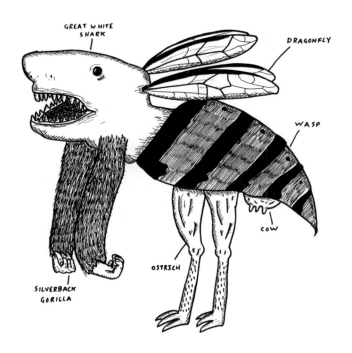

GREAT WHITE
SHARK

DRAGONFLY

WASP

COW

OSTRICH

SILVERBACK
GORILLA

ULTIMATE ANIMAL REMIX

Your challenge is to improve on nature by cross-breeding different species to create ultimate animals. Think of yourself as a Darwinian DJ and borrow bits and pieces from different creatures and then release your own unique remix.

You could create a beast that has all the evolutionary advantages of others. Or one that has all the disadvantages of others. Or maybe an animal remixed for a specific purpose or role in society.

STRETCH CHALLENGE
Create a short film about your creature, presented like a nature documentary.

CREATIVE KINSHIP

This challenge is set by guest challenger, polymath Adah Parris.

Adah is interested in kinship and the idea that it is about more than just our relationship with other human beings, it is about our relationship with all living things.

Adah's challenge is to use your imagination, your materials and your environment to create an artistic expression of what kinship is for you right now.

It can be as literal, whimsical or abstract as you like.

STRETCH CHALLENGE
Invite others of your kin to co-create your piece with you. (Humans, animals, plants, etc.)

ERIK'S MAKEOVER

Your challenge is to give Erik a make-over.

He has a big, important day ahead of him and
wants to look his best so I said he could use
a page of the book to get your help. I've no
idea what his important day is so you'll have
to guess for yourselves.

Copy/photograph/photoshop/draw Erik and use
your best fashion/makeup/lifestyle skills to
help him get ready.

STRETCH CHALLENGE
Create a number of different looks for Erik for
different occasions. A date, a job interview,
a casual Sunday afternoon, a high-powered
business meeting, an underground wrestling
match, etc.

POINTLESS PASTE-UPS

Create a poster with the sole intention of it having no point to it whatsoever and thereby confusing anyone who reads it.

Baffling headlines, unusual instructions, strange images with no explanation, random words, clubs to join that have no joining instructions, maps that show nothing. The trick here is to draw people in close, only to then scramble their brains.

The final step is to put your poster somewhere prominent to maximise the amount of people that will get to encounter it.

STRETCH CHALLENGE
You may want to make copies of your poster and create a concerted campaign of confusion.

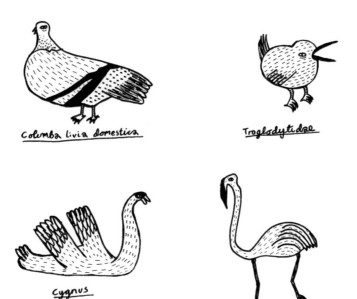

Columba livia domestica

Troglodytidae

Cygnus

Phoenicopterus

BADLY DRAWN BIRDS

This challenge is to draw some birds very badly.

Misshapen mallards, disproportioned doves, warped wrens. As long as you take great care to make them the worst drawings/paintings you have ever done they will be perfect responses to this challenge.

Although this challenge is called Badly DRAWN Birds you can use whatever medium you like – pen, paint, pencil, pastel, clay, interpretive dance, etc.

STRETCH CHALLENGE
Create a series of badly drawn birds and turn them into a ornithological guide.

MONOCHROME MAMMALS

Pick a mammal, pick a colour and then paint/draw/
sculpt your creature using varying tones of
only that colour. (I chose shades of green for
my lovely monochrome nutria.)

STRETCH CHALLENGE
Produce a series of images of your animal with
different monochrome colour schemes and sell
it as an exclusive pop-art collection.

PREDICT THE FUTURE

This challenge is set by guest challenger, surrealist comedian Michael Brunström.

Michael says that in the past, soothsayers looked at the movement of birds, the entrails of animals, lines on the hand or bumps on the head, the movement of stars and planets, tarot cards and tea leaves.

Your challenge is to invent a novel new way of predicting the future. For example, examine the patterns made by spilled coffee. Look out for unusual activity on the supermarket shelves. What secrets does your underwear reveal?

STRETCH CHALLENGE
Offer your future-prediction services to others.

DISCOUNT SUPERMARKET PRODUCT DESIGNER

You are invited to create some new product lines for discount supermarkets. Products that, at a glance, look exactly like a well known brand but on closer inspection are a very well-designed cheaper version.

There is a fine art to this job – you need to copy the colour-scheme, the font, the logo, the imagery, the slogans, etc. But, at the same time, make sure they're different enough to avoid any legal action from the owners of the real products.

STRETCH CHALLENGE
Go one further and create the actual product. Or film an advert for your cleverly disguised discount product.

DARE DICE

Create a dice that dares you to do stuff. What the stuff is is totally up to you.

It could be to do things you've always wanted to do but never had the excuse to. It could be to do things you've been procrastinating over. Or it might be random stuff such as JUMP UP AND DOWN SCREAMING, FIND A DOG TO STROKE, SING TO A STRANGER, ROTATE GENTLY FOR THE NEXT 3 MINUTES, etc.

You can use a dice you already have or make one. Use your dice throughout the day whenever you want to spice things up.

STRETCH CHALLENGE
Find a friend and make a dice for each other.

NOTE: I know the singular is "die" but it looks too weird in written form!

DOGS

YOU GOT IT GOING ON

MOTIVATIONAL POSTERS FOR ANIMALS

Your challenge is to make a motivational poster for the animals. Why should only human beings benefit from the inspirational power of this life-changing art form?

You could create a poster to galvanise a gerbil, excite an emu, inspire an ivory-billed woodpecker. As long as it leaves the animal feeling more empowered to actualise its full potential and unleash its very best self, it can be anything you like.

STRETCH CHALLENGE

Why not create a series of posters for different species? Or go to the zoo and spend an entire week/month making one for every single creature.

DRAW A WATCH ON YOUR ARM

Draw a watch on your arm. Your watch could be a digital one. An analogue one. A cheap one. An expensive one. What the watch is like is irrelevant. It is simply a watch you are proud of. During the day take a look at your watch and be reassured that you know what the time is.

If somebody asks you the time then you know what to do! In fact, why not walk around and ask people if they want to know what the time is or if they want to see your watch. If you normally wear a watch then take it off for the day. Or if you can't bear to be parted with it draw one on the other arm.

STRETCH CHALLENGE
Open a pop-up watch shop where you draw watches for people.

HOLD A HUMAN

This challenge is set by guest challenger, artist Vinca Petersen.

Vinca's challenge is to find another human being, hold hands with them and gently look into their eyes for 2 minutes.

Vinca suggests you should try to do it at least twice today. If you don't have another human to work with then simply hold your own hands and gently stare into your eyes in the mirror.

STRETCH CHALLENGE
See how many different human beings you can do this with and compare your experiences.

PAPER CUTTING PORTRAITS

Your challenge is to create a portrait using the beautifully imperfect medium of paper cutting using only paper/card/scissors/scalpel.

This challenge is much easier if you are not used to paper cutting. But if you are an accomplished paper cutter then maybe try this one with a non-dominant hand. (If you are confident you won't injure yourself in the process!)

STRETCH CHALLENGE
Do a portrait of more than one person. A band, a football team, a re-creation of your school class picture, etc.

INEXPERT TOUR GUIDE

Become an inexpert tour guide and imbue the landscape with your imagination. Wander around your town, city, office, home, school, estate, etc and improvise fascinating facts to delight your tourists.

There are two "moves" in Inexpert Tours:

MOVE 1: Be the tour guide and suddenly point something out to the other(s) and then tell them all about it.

MOVE 2: Be the tourist and point at something that catches your attention and ask the other(s) to tell you all about it.

STRETCH CHALLENGE
Make a sign and offer your services to actual tourists.

SURREALIST TIME CAPSULE

Make items for a weird, surrealist time capsule with the sole objective of confusing people in the future and make them question everything they thought they knew about the past.

Create newspaper headlines, diary entries, photographs, food stuff, weird toys/objects, descriptions of popular games – basically anything that will cause a futuristic moment of *"huh?"*

STRETCH CHALLENGE
Why not go a step further and actually bury your time capsule somewhere and sit back with the satisfaction that you will make the life of somebody a little bit more wonky long after you've gone.

LEN'S DANCE MOVES #34

ESCAPE THE KILLER BEES

| MOVE 1 | MOVE 2 | MOVE 3 |
| SHOO THE BEES | FLEE THE BEES | CLIMB OVER THE STYLE |

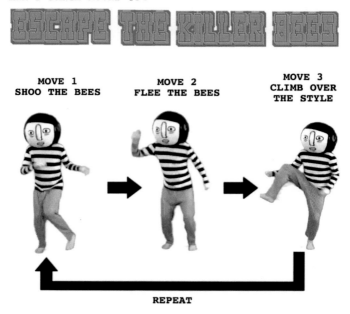

REPEAT

INVENT A DANCE

Invent a brand new dance with a sequenced set of named dance moves.

Take time to choreograph and name a number of unique moves based on physical actions and teach them to others through providing an illustrated guide to your dance or videoing your own performance.

Don't forget to name your dance as well as the moves within it.

STRETCH CHALLENGE
Compose a piece of music to accompany your dance moves.

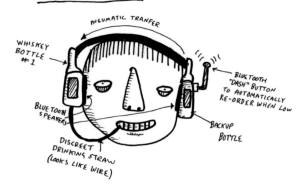

WHISKEY HEADPHONES

PNEUMATIC TRANFER

WHISKEY BOTTLE #1

BLUE TOOTH "DASH" BUTTON TO AUTOMATICALLY RE-ORDER WHEN LOW

BLUE TOOTH SPEAKERS

BACKUP BOTTLE

DISCREET DRINKING STRAW (LOOKS LIKE WIRE)

REALITY REMIX

This challenge is set by guest challengers Rosie and Faris Yakob of Genius Steals.

Choose two random things you come across. They can be physical items, or things you see in the paper/on tv/billboards/online. There must be two of them though. Once you have two, combine them to invent something that solves a problem. It can be real, it can be silly, it doesn't matter.

Present your remixes as a drawing, a mock up, a prototype or in any other way that comes to mind.

STRETCH CHALLENGE

Conduct some public research to see what people think of your invention and then take it from concept to market in a single day.

The following labels appear on the collage:

FLAT CAP FOR WARMTH

HIGHLY SENSITIVE EARS

360 SWIVLY EYES

ATTACK STANCE TO HYPNOTISE PREY

BLUE BLOOD

REGINA DIABLO

REGINA DIABLO IS A MYTHICAL BEAST THAT LIVES ON THE ROCKY OUTCROP OF BEMBRIDGE BEACH ON THE ISLE OF WIGHT.

IT LIVES ON CRABS WHICH IT CONFUSES WITH ITS GOOFY TEETH BEFORE STINGING THEM TO DEATH WITH ITS POISONED ARSE.

IT HAS BEEN KNOWN TO OCCASIONALLY CONSUME DOGS + SMALL CHILDREN.

FAST RUNNING LEGS

POISON STING

#FWTFEB

@stevexoh

MYTHICAL BEAST COLLAGE

Create a mythical beast from bits and pieces of magazines, newspapers, catalogues, flyers, photographs, etc. Give your beast a name and add details about its habitat, history, food, habits, etc. The more nerdy the detail the better.

STRETCH CHALLENGE

Create a whole guidebook of mythical beasts that can be found in a particular place with a map to show what lives where.

Or a food-chain of mythical beasts. What eats what? What is the incredibly delicate and symbiotic mythical beast eco-system?

9th FEBRUARY 2020: CHECKLIST

- NUMBER OF DOGS STROKED ☐
- NUMBER OF SWEAR WORDS USED ☐
  (LIST THEM HERE: _____)
- BREAK A RULE ☐
- HELP SOMEONE ☐
- LOSE AN ARGUMENT ☐
- NUMBER OF CELEBRITIES STROKED ☐
- NUMBER OF SHOP KEEPERS CONFUSED ☐
- SPIN AROUND SHOUTING "COOOLZ!" ☐
- NUMBER OF TIMES SAYING "LITERALLY" ☐
  WHEN IT IS ACTUALLY LITERAL
- WEAR SLIPPERS IN PUBLIC ☑

TOTAL ☐

@STEVExoh

#WTFEB

SCORE THE DAY

Create a scorecard/checklist for the day. What stuff do you want to do? What things do you want to see? Some items could be a simple yes/no check box. Some could be a tally that you accumulate throughout the day. But the most important thing is to try to make them as weird and wonky as possible.

Make some utterly baffling or impossible – you never know if the act of writing them down will make them come true! If you want to make it look/feel even more official then carry your card around on a clipboard all day.

STRETCH CHALLENGE
Swap scorecards with somebody else.

NON-LEAGUE FOOTBALL BADGES

I've a theory that non-league and lower league football (soccer) clubs have much weirder badges than the top clubs. They often feature things such as animals, pirates, wizards, mythical creatures, oddly specific buildings, strange abstract images, bizarre club mottos.

I assume this is because they don't have the big design budgets of the top clubs to overly style their brand and instead get someone they know to knock one together. They are amazing and long may this continue.

So, your challenge is to design a weird badge for an obscure non-league football club in all its nonsensical glory.

STRETCH CHALLENGE
You could actually embroider a badge. Or design a whole kit to attach your badge onto.

GIVE IT AWAY NOW

Your challenge is to create a beautiful piece of art with the sole purpose of setting it free and never knowing its fate.

It could be a drawing, a painting, a thing you make. The only rule is that once it is finished you need to leave it in a public space for somebody else to find and then walk away.

How does it feel to take your time making something and then setting it free?

STRETCH CHALLENGE
Create a whole series of things to give away and spend the day creating a little trail of magic and mystery.

MOVE BEYOND WORDS

This challenge is set by the pioneering dyslexic arts organisation Move Beyond Words.

Begin by picking a word, any word, and respond to it in an intuitive, creative way.

You might be inspired to move or dance in response to the shape and feel of the word, sing or perform it, write a piece of music or create a piece of art that takes you deeper into the feel of the word. Or you might represent the word in shapes, food, etchings in the sand, traces in the bathroom mirror.

STRETCH CHALLENGE
Create an entire film, cartoon strip, dance, opera, etc inspired by your word.

TURN LITTER INTO ART

This challenge is to turn litter into art. It has been inspired by the work of Ben Wilson, aka Chewing Gum Man, who turns pieces of discarded chewing gum into tiny painted master-pieces. (An example of Ben's work is shown in this picture.)

You might create a sculpture from empty cans, turn abandoned newspaper into origami, create an opera using discarded cigarette butts.

As long as you turn something thoughtless into something magical, it really doesn't matter.

STRETCH CHALLENGE
Why not create an exhibition of your litter art to inspire others to do the same?

I don't KNOW what I'd DO WITHOUT YOU,
AND all THE things THAT YOU PROVIDE,
Your OBLONG mouth THAT sure defines YOU,
AND lets ME PUT MY POST INSIDE.

BUT YOU must GET SO cold and LONELY,
IN the MIDDLE OF the NIGHT
Whilst I'm in BED SO warm + COSY,
— It breaks MY heart, IT DON'T feel right.

ONE DAY I'll PRIZE you FROM THE PAVEMENT,
AND bring YOU HOME with ME,
LIBERATE you FROM enslavement,
AND make LASAGNE for your tea.

INANIMATE OBJECT LOVE SONGS

Write a love song for an inanimate object.

Why should such moving and heartfelt compositions be limited to sentient beings? This is an opportunity to express your affections for your toaster or to boldly declare your devotion to a favourite spanner or tell the world about your undying love for a flip flop. It can be anything so don't hold back.

STRETCH CHALLENGE
You may want to record your song or set it to music so that even more of the love and raw emotion can be experienced by others.

Or take it a step further and sing it from your window, perform it on the street, or at an open mic.

I DON'T KNOW DAY

This challenge is all about practicing not knowing and answering any questions you are asked by saying "I don't know".

Ideally it will be truthful which means you might have to seek out people, conversations and situations where you genuinely don't know. But if you can't do that just say "I DON'T KNOW" to every question you are asked and see what happens.

Try and do this at least 20 times to really experience the power of not knowing. And remember, to get the full experience, don't tell anyone you are doing this challenge.

STRETCH CHALLENGE
Can you do it for a full day/week/month/life-time?

THE AMAZING EMOTION OSCILLATOR

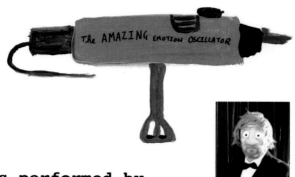

As performed by
Mr Lembitt Shuttleservice

INSTRUMENTS OF HOPE

This challenge is set by guest challenger, handsome Sagittarius Dr Paul Taylor Pitt. Dr Paul's challenge is to invent a musical instrument from items you have laying around the home/office/wherever you are.

It could be a stringed instrument, a wind instrument, some sort of electronic instrument As long as you have made it, it doesn't matter.

What's most important is that your instrument should have a unique purpose to it. Maybe it produces a sound that inspires HOPE, a tone that engenders LOVE or a resonance that can't help but stimulate POSITIVE CHANGE in the world.

STRETCH CHALLENGE
Put on a concert for others so your instrument can start to have an impact on humanity.

THE WRONG MATERIALS

Your challenge is to make some art using the wrong materials.

You can paint, draw, sculpt, whatever you want, as long as it is made with materials and tools not designed to make art with. (I used coffee, tomato puree, ketchup and Siracha sauce in the image above and painted it using a toothpick and a small cork.)

STRETCH CHALLENGE
Create a series of works using inappropriate materials. Or if you really want to torture yourself you could illustrate a comic strip or create an entire graphic novel.

SHAKESPEAREAN BILLBOARD ANNOUNCER

Your challenge is to narrate adverts, signs, billboards, products, etc, as if you are a classically trained Shakespearean actor who is delivering a deeply profound sonnet.

Remember everything from your training. Take your time before you speak. Deep breaths. Good posture. Vary the cadence, volume and emotion in your voice. And don't forget to make big sweeping gestures with your arms as you tell your adoring audience the words they are just dying to hear.

Remember to pause for applause when you have finished.

STRETCH CHALLENGE
Offer your services by sending recordings to the various companies you promote.

BAD ORIGAMI

Origami is the art of paper folding, no cutting, no tape, no tearing.

Your challenge is to do the opposite and break all the rules.

You could create an animal, a human, a flower, an amazing replica of a famous landmark. As long as it is bad it is good.

STRETCH CHALLENGE

Why not create a menagerie of bad origami animals? Or a line up of awful origami humans? Or open your own gallery of terrible origami?

WTFEB SPIN-OFF PROJECT

The final challenge for this book is to channel the creative spirit of WTFEB into your very own spin-off project.

Your spin-off project might be inspired by your favourite challenge from the book or it might be an experiment inspired by a thing you've discovered about yourself through completing the challenges.

You might start a wonky life drawing class, a boring poetry club, a low-budget film studio, a fortune telling service or anything else that continues to embolden the creatively wonky spirit of WTFEB.

The most important thing is that your spin-off project is something NEW that you will launch TODAY.

Further resources
There are a load of additional resources for these challenges online including a dice template, how to make a zine, a printable Erik to makeover, videos of various challenges and lots more.

Visit www.wtfeb.com

Thank you to ...
Every single person who took part in WTFEB, whether you did all the challenges, some of them, or watched from the sidelines. Thanks to the wonderful proof-readers @stephupontheearth, @sam_zog, @dorotheegigan, @echo.kilo.foxtrot, @feelmorecreative and @elfriniel.

A big thanks to Nick Parker and jdwoof for being wise sounding-boards throughout the process of making this book and thanks to Maya for suggesting I do one big final WTFEB in 2023.

and thanks to all the WTFEB guest challengers
ERIC13: @eric13000
Nick Parker: www.nickparker.co.uk
Lesley Graney/RAON: @randomactsofnonsense
Pippa Evans: @iampippaevans
Jo Wood: @jdwoof
Kazland: @kazland
Mark Shayler: @markshayler
Reasons to be Cheerful: @manyreasonstobecheerful
Revolting Rosy Pendlebaby: @revoltingrosy
Ben Murphie: @benmurphie
JP Flintoff: www.flintoff.org
Kath of Feel More Creative: @feelmorecreative
Robert Poynton: www.robertpoynton.com
Katie Elliott: www.littlechallenges.com
Amy Kean: @amyckean
Adah Parris: www.adahparris.com
Michael Brunström: @michaelbrunstrom
Vinca Petersen: @vincapetersen
Rosie & Faris Yakob: @rosieyakob @farisy
Move Beyond Words: www.movebeyondwords.co.uk
Dr Paul Taylor-Pitt: @drpaultaylorpitt

And a final thanks to YOU for buying this book and supporting my work. It means a lot. x